SAINTS alive

Healing in the Church

LINK-WORK BOOK

ROGER M. VAUGHAN

provider
helping you to help others

ISBN 1 84291 041 8

Published by
KINGSWAY COMMUNICATIONS LTD
Lottbridge Drove, Eastbourne, BN23 6NT, England.
Email: books@kingsway.co.uk
in association with
Anglican Renewal Ministries
4 Bramble Street, Derby DE1 1HU.
Email: saintsalive@anglican-renewal.org.uk

Book design and production for the publishers by
Bookprint Creative Services, P.O. Box 827, BN21 3YJ, England.
Printed in Great Britain.

Contents

Outline of the course

▶ Session 1

What do we mean by 'healing'? Is it an event or a process? Healing and wholeness.

▶ Session 2

The healing ministry of Jesus. Looking at the variety of ways he healed people. Four basic kinds of healing in a person.

▶ Session 3

Approaches to healing – Christian and others. How does the Christian ministry of healing relate to medical science and alternative and complementary methods of healing?

▶ Session 4

The part played by faith. The relationship between faith and action in the Christian ministry of healing.

▶ Session 5

A further look at the healing ministry of Jesus. What are our hopes and fears as we consider the possibility that Jesus is calling us into this ministry?

▶ Session 6

How can we be filled with the Holy Spirit, to equip us for this ministry?

▶ Session 7

Questions about God and the mystery of suffering, 'unanswered prayer', and death. How can we believe in a good, all-powerful and loving God?

(Note: This session may be used at any time during the course as seems appropriate.)

▶ Session 8

What are the key guidelines for good practice in this ministry? What concerns are raised about ministering to those who have been involved in the occult? How can we safely pray with children? How should we react to outward, visible signs of what we believe to be the Holy Spirit's activity?

▶ Session 9

What do we mean by 'the healing of emotions and memories'? What steps should a local church take to set up a recognised and effective ministry of healing?

Making the most of the course

'When Jesus had called the Twelve together, he gave them power and authority to drive out all demons and to cure diseases, and he sent them out to preach the kingdom of God and to heal the sick.'   (Luke 9:1–2)

▶ Introduction

Try to set aside 15 minutes each day to be quiet and draw close to God. Choose a time of the day when you are not too tired, and won't be interrupted. Find a place where you can be by yourself and can relax. The daily readings are designed to help you to read your Bible and to pray. They supplement the teaching given during the course, and are usually based on the previous week's sessions.

For each week of the nine week course you will find some suggestions for your private study set out in the following way:

- A short summary of the main themes of the teaching at your group session.
- Five suggestions for daily readings. One of these will be labelled 'for contemplation'.
- A 'chunk reading' which takes fairly long passages from the Bible and asks you to read them straight through. The chunk reading is divided into two parts for days 6 and 7 of the week. You could, of course, make it a one-day exercise if you wish.
- A space for your own notes, or questions that you want to raise with your group leader privately or at the next group meeting.

▶ Using the link-work books as a basis for personal prayer

Prayer is simply being in a real living relationship with God. There is no correct way to pray. 'Pray as you can, not as you can't!' However, the following comments may be helpful. Find a place and time where you can regularly meet with God. Choose a body position which enables you to concentrate.

Talk to God naturally. Learn to ask questions and then to wait in stillness to see if there is an answer. When words come to your mind, believe that they are from God.

There are many different ways of arranging your prayer time. If you do not have a 'shape' to your prayer time, the following pattern might fit well with your link-work.

- *Praise* will focus your attention on God. You might sing a song or hymn, or read a psalm of praise.
- *Getting straight!* There may be things that you need to talk through with God, eg sins to be confessed, or worries to be brought to him.
- *Others.* Pray for the group members and those in need who are being prayed for by your group.
- *Listen to God's word.* Now turn to your daily reading task. Ask the Holy Spirit to teach you through this reading.
- *Thanksgiving.* Thank God for what he has done for you and for others.
- *Be still.* Don't rush into the next job at this point. Try to be still for a few moments, soaking up his presence.

Remember these are only ideas. If this pattern is not right for you, try one that is. If you are not sure what to do, talk it through with your group leader.

▶ Using the 'contemplation' verses

The verse for contemplation is normally set on the fourth day of the week. Whereas the other daily readings require you to think about their meaning, the contemplative exercise is different. You should aim to relax and simply let the verse 'soak into' you. Carry the verse with you in your mind throughout the day. 'Let the word of Christ dwell in you richly' (Colossians 3:16).

▶ Keeping a journal during the course

The link-work should become the basis of a personal journal. Many people today are discovering the value of such journals. If the space provided in this link-work book is not enough, start a small notebook. After the group sessions, write down anything that seemed especially important to you. In the same way, jot down notes in your journal after each session with the link-work book. Here are the kinds of questions or thoughts that you might ask yourself as you go through the course:

- In what ways have I sensed God speaking to me?
- What ideas have seemed important or new to me?
- How have I sensed God enriching my life as the course goes on?

Jot down questions that you want to ask at the next session. Make a note when you feel strongly about some part of the course, trying to summarise your feelings. Record, with thanksgiving, any answers to prayer that you may have experienced.

Remember this is your journal. Be as imaginative in its use as you like.

▶ Praying for others

Immediately prior to the daily Bible readings there is a page where you can fill in the names of those who are sharing the course with you, so that you can remember them daily in your prayers as you come to do your link-work. Your group will be richly blessed by this mutual prayer.

There is also a second space for the names of a few people for whom the group will pray during the course. These will be selected at the first meeting. You may have a friend who is in need of prayer at this time. You will be encouraged to let everyone in the group share in prayer for this person.

▶ Appendix A – The questionnaire

At the end of the link-work book are several appendices. Appendix A is a short questionnaire. Your group leader will introduce this around the fifth session of the course. Do not be alarmed by this. It is designed to help you and your leader know where you are in your thinking about the Christian healing ministry.

▶ Appendix B – The accounts of healing in the ministry of Jesus

You may wish to refer to this as a supplement to your daily reading, or use it as a basis for your own Bible study after the course has finished.

▶ Appendix C – The prayer of commitment

God longs to give us his love and his power by filling us with the Holy Spirit. The short prayer in Appendix C is one simple way of praying for people to be baptised in the power of the Holy Spirit.

▶ Appendix D – Guidelines for good practice

As the Christian healing ministry has gained ground, the need for guidelines for good practice has become necessary. The guidelines printed in the link-work book are draft guidelines from the House of Bishops.

▶ Appendix E – Ten principles for helping people who have been involved with the occult

Many people who join the church and are concerned about the healing ministry have been searching for answers to the great questions of life. Their journey has sometimes involved contact with occult practices. The ten principles listed in this appendix are designed to help us minister to such people. They need our love and guidance, not our condemnation. Sadly there have been cases where such people have felt shunned by Christians. We need to show warmth and love to them, but at the same time recognise the particular skills and approaches needed in ministering to them.

Praying for others

▶ Your group

Write the names of the leaders and members of your group below. Try to remember them each day in your prayers either before or after your Bible reading. The prayer in Ephesians 3:14–21 may help you sum up your prayers:

For this reason I kneel before the Father, from whom his whole family in heaven and on earth derives its name. I pray that out of his glorious riches he may strengthen you with power through his Spirit in your inner being, so that Christ may dwell in your hearts through faith. And I pray that you, being rooted and established in love, may have power, together with all the saints, to grasp how wide and long and high and deep is the love of Christ, and to know this love that surpasses knowledge – that you may be filled to the measure of all the fullness of God. Now to him who is able to do immeasurably more than all we ask or imagine, according to his power that is at work within us, to him be glory in the church and in Christ Jesus throughout all generations, for ever and ever! Amen.

Name	Notes

Name	Notes

▶ Those with particular needs

During the course your group will remember a few people who have particular needs. You will be asked to enter their names here during the first week, and to continue to remember them. There is a column for their names, and next to it is space to note how God honours your prayers. Past experience has shown that this simple commitment to prayer has led to some remarkable signs of God's healing love in the lives of those for whom we have prayed.

Name	Prayer requirements

May God himself, the God of peace, sanctify you through and through. May your whole spirit, soul and body be kept blameless at the coming of our Lord Jesus Christ. The one who calls you is faithful and he will do it. (1 Thessalonians 5:23–24)

1 What do we mean by 'healing'?

▶ Healing as a process

The Christian healing ministry should draw everyone involved into a new or stronger relationship with Jesus. 'Healing is Jesus Christ meeting us at our point of need' (Bishop Morris Maddocks). The process involves discovering that something is wrong; admitting the problem; seeking and accepting help; adopting a new lifestyle where necessary.

▶ Healing as wholeness

The biblical concept of healing is very broad, and is summed up in the word *shalom*. This has many meanings, including peace, integrity, harmony and physical and mental health. This wholeness – which encompasses our relationship with God, with others, with ourselves, and with God's world – has become distorted and fragmented. The healing ministry seeks to reintegrate this fragmentation.

▶ Ways of praying for healing (1)

Pray as you can, not as you can't. However, be prepared for the Holy Spirit to open up new ways of praying.

 Daily Bible readings

---

Luke 4:14–30 – The mission of Jesus

Jesus quotes Isaiah 61 at the start of his ministry at Nazareth. By doing so he was declaring that the Messiah, who had been awaited for so long, had now come. The outward 'signs and wonders' would give authenticity to his claim. Note too the hostility that this claim brings to him. The healing ministry is costly.

Mark 3:13–19 – Jesus calls us into the ministry of healing

Jesus calls those he wants! Before the disciples could be sent out, they had to be 'with him'. Ask yourself if you believe that you are called into this new and exciting venture by Jesus. He calls you, like the disciples, to be with him and ultimately to be sent out with his authority. How do you feel about this?

John 9:1–34 – Healing events and the healing process

Make a list of the events that take place in the process of the blind man's healing.

Mark 6:53–56 – Verses for contemplation

These verses summarise the healing ministry of Jesus. Use the last phrase for contemplation: 'All who touched him were healed.'

1 Thessalonians 5:12–28 – Body, soul and spirit

This final instruction from one of the earliest of Paul's letters includes these words:

> May God himself, the God of peace, sanctify you through and through. May your whole spirit, soul and body be kept blameless at the coming of our Lord Jesus Christ. The one who calls you is faithful and he will do it.

Healing is not just a matter of bodily healing but a process towards the integration of the complete person – body, soul and spirit. It is about wholeness.

Chunk readings

 Luke chapters 4–7

 Luke 8:1–10:24

Luke was a doctor, so he would have been interested in the healings that took place when Jesus was on earth. Note in particular that Luke describes how Jesus shared this ministry with the disciples (see Luke 9:1–2 and Luke 10:1–24). Note too the variety of healings. You might like to make a list of them in your journal.

▶ Notes

SESSION

2 The healing ministry of Jesus (Part 1)

▶ Knowing Jesus the healer

'A Christian can never discuss healing without having Jesus in mind' (Bishop Morris Maddocks).

Jesus sees each situation and person as a special and individual case. We do not discover techniques for our own ministry when we look at the Gospels. Rather we come to know Jesus better, and therefore become more open to the inner prompting of his Spirit in us.

▶ Four basic kinds of healing

Francis MacNutt, in *Healing*, identified four basic types of healing. They overlap and there are no clear divisions. They are: physical healing, emotional healing, healing of the diseased spirit, and deliverance.

▶ Ways of praying for healing (2)

The laying on of hands

The laying on of hands should be done with prayer, love and gentleness. It should not be oppressive, dominating, or abusive. Remember that the laying on of hands is not magic, but a sign and symbol of God's love and power. Accept that there may be outward signs of the Holy Spirit's presence and power.

 Daily Bible readings

---

 DAY 1 ### Luke 4:31–44 – Contrasts

Note the contrast between public (the healing of the man with an evil spirit in the synagogue) and private (the healing of Simon's mother-in-law in the privacy of her own home). There is also the contrast between the crowds milling round Jesus as soon as the Sabbath was over, and Jesus in solitary prayer at daybreak.

 DAY 2 ### John 9:35–41 – Deeds and words

John often uses the mighty works of Jesus as spring-boards for further teaching. Here the story of the healing of the man born blind is the event that leads to teaching about spiritual blindness. It is the first miracle to follow the claim, 'I am the light of the world' (John 8:12). Pray that Jesus will open your eyes as you follow through this course on the ministry of healing.

 DAY 3 ### Mark 1:40–45 – The importance of touch

Reaching out to people, touching people, allowing them to touch us, and communicating the loving touch of God through these actions is an important way of praying for people. It conveys both human sympathy and divine power.

 DAY 4 ### John 15:4 – Verse for contemplation

Consider each of the three phrases separately, and finally join them together.

- 'Remain in me, and I will remain in you.'
- 'No branch can bear fruit by itself; it must remain in the vine.'
- 'Neither can you bear fruit unless you remain in me.'

Luke 17:11–19 – Thanksgiving

This famous encounter of Jesus with the ten lepers underlines the importance of thanksgiving. Does thankfulness play a major part in your life? Write a list of things for which you should give thanks today.

Chunk readings

Mark chapters 1–5

Mark 6:1–9:37

Mark gives a vivid account of the ministry of Jesus. The disciples seem to fail to grasp who Jesus is until Peter confesses that Jesus is the Christ (8:29). The failure of the disciples to heal the boy with the evil spirit (Mark 9:1–32), and their pitiful squabbling about who was greatest are sad reflections on them. However, just turn to the very last verse of the Gospel (Mark 16:20) which shows us what they were to become. Don't be discouraged!

▶ **Notes**

3 Approaches to healing – Christian and others

▶ Healing and medicine

Medical science is a fundamental part of God's healing grace, but we should not confine God's healing love to medicine alone.

▶ Various views about the Christian ministry of healing

1. *The booster rocket*. Healings took place in the earliest days of the church but have now ceased.
2. *Saints and shrines*. Healing only comes through special people or places.
3. *The sacraments*. Healing should only be expected during the official ministry of the church.
4. *Every member*. All Christians should expect to be able to minister healing.
5. *Faith healing and psychic gifts*. Healing comes as a special power to those with psychic gifts.

▶ Alternative therapies – are they counterfeit? How can we tell?

With the huge range of alternative and complementary methods of healing used today we have to try to discern whether any particular method is a simple application of God-given gifts 'in creation', some form of satanic counterfeit, or just dangerous nonsense.

▶ Ways of praying for healing (3)

Developing listening skills, both at a human level and for listening to God.

 ## Daily Bible readings

 ### Ephesians 1:1–14 – God's great plan

God's plan for us all is unity and harmony restored under the headship of Jesus Christ. Write a list of all the things that God has done for you through Jesus, based on this passage. Is your life sealed with the Holy Spirit (verse 13)?

 ### Job 2:11–13 – 'Listening is a healing activity' (Angela Ashwin)

Job's comforters sat with him for seven days. During this long time they said nothing. Pray that God will develop your listening skills, as these are essential in the ministry of healing. What practical steps are you taking to train yourself to be a better listener?

1 Samuel 3:1–19

We must learn how to listen to God. Samuel learns the lesson for the first time. Do you believe that God wants to speak to you? Do you give time to listen to God? In your prayer time try repeating your own name a couple of times . . . and then listen!

Verse for contemplation

Contrast Proverbs 18:13 – 'He who answers before listening – that is his folly and his shame' – with 1 Samuel 3:10b – 'Then Samuel said, "Speak, for your servant is listening."' Use this final phrase as a verse for contemplation.

Exodus 7:8–13 – Counterfeit signs

As we look at various alternative therapies we need to decide if some are counterfeits. This Old Testament passage illustrates vividly how God's signs and wonders can be mimicked.

Chunk readings

Genesis chapters 1–5

Genesis 6:1–11:8

The first eleven chapters of Genesis describe the beauty and order of God's creation as he intended it, and the subsequent 'fragmentation' which comes as a result of the Fall. See how various aspects of the initial harmony are destroyed. Adam and Eve's relationship with God, with one another and with the world in which they are placed is spoilt. See how sin brings death and destruction, and note too the splitting up of people into different language speaking groups (Genesis 11:1–8). In spite of this, God still labours to save humankind; his love is still constant.

▶ Notes

4 The part played by faith

▶ Faith in the ministry of Jesus

Faith is a basic trust in God. As we begin to live by faith, it becomes 'visible'. Whenever Jesus healed people faith was in evidence, always in Jesus himself, but also sometimes evident in the people seeking healing, or on the part of those seeking healing for their friends.

▶ A gift of faith (1 Corinthians 12:9)

A gift of faith is a deep, overwhelming conviction that God will act in a particular way. Continual use of gifts of faith encourage the growth of faith as a fruit of the Holy Spirit (Galatians 5:22).

▶ Faith when things get tough

Difficult times test our faith. We must keep looking at Jesus, not the problem, and we will need to rely on one another for support. Our faith can be built up by reading faith-building books, listening to encouraging tapes and so on.

▶ Ways of praying for healing (4)

Building up our faith and dealing with doubts.

 Daily Bible readings

---

 Hebrews 11:1–40 – People of faith

After defining what faith is, the writer of the epistle to the Hebrews goes on to list examples of people of faith. We think of them as heroes and heroines but we must remember that they were ordinary people 'just like us' (James 5:17). 'I do not have great faith, but I have faith in a great God' (Corrie Ten Boom). In what ways is your faith growing as you share in this course?

 Matthew 14:22–36 – Fix your eyes on Jesus

As long as Peter looks at Jesus he can walk on the water. The moment he looks at the waves, he sinks. What problems stop you looking at Jesus? Ask the Lord for grace to keep looking at him, not at the problems.

 Mark 6:1–6 – Unbelief

Even the ministry of Jesus was limited by a climate of unbelief. (Note too how Jesus put those who did not believe out of the room before he healed the daughter of Jairus in Mark 5:35–43.)

 Mark 9:23 – Verse for contemplation

'Everything is possible for him who believes.'

 Mark 2:5; Luke 8:48 – Visible faith

Faith is made visible by our actions. These readings are just two illustrations of this principle. In what ways does your life demonstrate your faith?

Chunk readings

Acts chapters 1–5

Acts chapters 6–9

Faith is made visible by actions. As we look at the opening chapters of Acts, we see how different the disciples are from how they were in Mark 10. Now they are filled with the power of the Holy Spirit, and the Lord works with them confirming his word by the signs that accompany it (see Mark 16:20). Note too the persecution and suffering that accompanies the ministry (Acts 4). The healing ministry is costly (Isaiah 53).

▶ Notes

5 The healing ministry of Jesus (Part 2)

▶ Balance in the ministry of Jesus

As we look at the ministry of Jesus we note a balance between his

- private and public life
- words and actions
- human love and divine power

Jesus saw healing as a sign of the coming of the kingdom of God on earth. He encouraged others to share in it (Luke 9–10).

▶ Ways of praying for healing (5)

Prayer in tongues. Why is this gift so useful and how can we pray in tongues?

It is beneficial

- in our relationship with God
- in the church
- as a sign to unbelievers

Daily Bible readings

Mark 16:9–20 – The experience of the early church

It is generally accepted that this ending to Mark's Gospel was added at a later date to the original writing. This does not mean that we can dismiss it, for it describes the experience of the early Christians as they stepped out in faith and love.

Luke 8:26–39 – Healing is costly

Ponder the story of the healing of the demon-possessed man. What facets of your own character do you wish could be drowned? Ask God to help you deal with them. Think about the cost of this healing: to the man, to the people of the Gerasenes, to the owner of the pigs, and especially to Jesus himself.

---

2 Kings 5 – The healing of Naaman

This healing leads to an acknowledgement that 'there is no God in all the world except in Israel' (v15). True healing always leads us to the one true God. 'For me to be healed was to be taken more deeply into God, to plumb more fully the mystery of his power and love' (Jane Grayshon, *A Pathway through Pain*). Note too the gift of wisdom given to Naaman's servants to persuade their master to bathe in the river Jordan (v13).

Romans 12:2 – Verse for contemplation

All too frequently we allow our thinking and conse-quently our actions to be squeezed into the mould of worldly thinking. Paul urges us, 'Do not conform any longer to the pattern of this world, but be transformed by the renewing of your mind.'

1 Corinthians 12:1–11 – A list of spiritual gifts

Spiritual gifts are given to us for the common good. They are to be desired. They are to be used. They are to be shared. They are to be cherished. They are for us today. If you have any questions about them, write them down now and bring your questions to the group.

Chunk readings

2 Corinthians chapters 1–7

2 Corinthians chapters 8–13

This is an intensely personal letter. It often contrasts human weakness with the indwelling strength of Christ. To use one of Paul's analogies we are like 'jars of clay' containing Jesus Christ like a treasure. We may feel uncertain of the way ahead. Our work for Christ does not depend upon us, but upon his abiding presence in us through his Holy Spirit.

▶ **Notes**

6 Equipped for ministry

▶ Filled with the Holy Spirit

There are five key biblical words for those seeking the release of the Holy Spirit's power in their lives:

- Thirst (John 7:37)
- Repent (Acts 2:38)
- Ask (Luke 11:1–13)
- Believe (Luke 11:10–13)
- Obey (Acts 5:32)

Read about the gifts of the Holy Spirit and how they relate to healing (1 Corinthians 12).

The Holy Spirit is sometimes described in the Scriptures in terms of rivers of living water. How can we be effective channels of the life-giving Holy Spirit?

▶ Praying for healing (6)

During this session prayer will be made for group members to be filled with the Holy Spirit – to equip them for ministry. There is also an exploration of methods of intercessory prayer.

 Daily Bible readings

---

 ### Luke 11:1–13 – Praying for the Spirit

Luke records a summary of Jesus' teaching on prayer. From verse 5 onwards he is concerned with how we should pray for the Holy Spirit. What lessons can be drawn from this passage?

 ### Ezekiel 47:1–12 and Joel 3:17–19 – The Holy Spirit flows like a river

The analogy of God's love flowing like a river from his temple, bringing healing to the world, is taken up in Revelation 22. See also Psalm 1:1–3.

 ### John 7:37–44 – Through Jesus the Holy Spirit can flow from us

Streams of living water will flow from those who have been filled with the Holy Spirit's power.

 ### John 7:37–38 – Verse for contemplation

Jesus stood and said in a loud voice, 'If a man is thirsty, let him come to me and drink. Whoever believes in me, as the Scripture has said, streams of living water will flow from within him.'

 ### Acts 19:1–7 – Have *you* received the Holy Spirit?

Paul could tell that the people of Ephesus had not been filled with the power of the Holy Spirit. He ministered to them and they received this great blessing. Have you asked to be baptised in the power of the Holy Spirit?

(Your group leader may use the prayer in Appendix C. Read it through and think about what it means to you.)

Chunk readings

 John chapters 11–12

 John chapters 13–17

▶ Notes

7 God and the mystery of suffering

▶ How can a good God allow suffering?

Here we look at some of the difficult questions about suffering, death and 'unanswered' prayer. There are many questions that have to be faced but perhaps the most difficult are:

- How can we square our understanding of an all powerful and all loving God with the fact of suffering in our world?
- For Christians who have seen wonderful healings take place after prayer has been offered there is a further question: 'Why do such healings seem to be so arbitrary?'

▶ Ways of praying for healing (7)

The first question to ask is, 'Lord, is there something that needs healing in me?' Perhaps it is a bad relationship or a root of bitterness (Matthew 5:23–24).

Daily Bible readings

Isaiah 53 – The suffering servant

Underline or write out the verses which speak to you in this wonderful prophecy.

Mark 15:16–39 – The mocking, crucifixion and death of Jesus

Mark's account of the crucifixion is stark and dramatic. The centurion who watches the event is led to the point of faith. Salvation and healing are won for us by the Son of God who suffers and dies for the world. We enter into the mystery of suffering as we enter into the mystery of the cross.

Luke 8:40–56 – Chronic and acute conditions

Luke makes the point that the woman's sickness had been part of her life for twelve years. This represents the total life time of the young girl who had died. Long-term illness is draining physically, emotionally and spiritually. The chronic sick can often be taken for granted and even forgotten. Jesus finds time for the chronic sick even in the midst of an emergency. What lessons can you learn from this passage?

---

2 Timothy 1:7 – Verse for contemplation

'For God did not give us a spirit of timidity, but a spirit of power, of love and of self-discipline.'

Philippians 1:29–2:11 – The Servant King

It is granted to us not only to believe in Jesus but also to suffer for him. We must be like our master, who emptied himself for others. We may be called to 'enter into' the suffering of others. The healing ministry is glorious but costly. (Note that suffering in this context means suffering persecution not sickness.)

Chunk readings

Job chapters 1–9

Job chapters 38–42

The book of Job is a literary masterpiece. It has been a source of inspiration to countless people who have found themselves asking the question 'Why?' in the face of suffering. Suffering needs to be approached not so much as a problem to be solved but as a mystery to be entered into. In the book of Job, we find ourselves entering into this mystery, and deeply into the mind of one who suffers.

▶ Notes

8 Our ministry in practice

▶ Guidelines for good practice

Good practice is important in the Christian ministry of healing. We will be concerned to develop our own spirituality. All that we do should honour God and bring his love to those who seek our help. We will discuss the importance of:

- working in teams
- keeping confidences
- working under supervision
- being aware of our own limitations

Areas which cause particular concern are explored including the special needs of children and helping those involved in the occult.

This healing ministry may involve us in spiritual warfare. We need to rely upon Jesus and only minister with his power and authority. The authority of Jesus is given to the church and we must follow any guidelines laid down by our own church in dealing with these difficult cases. This work will involve listening, praying for peace, and seeking help from those who have authority to work in this area.

▶ Ways of praying for healing (8)

The prayer of command. As we learn to accept the power and authority which Jesus gives his disciples, we may find ourselves commanding sickness to leave a person.

 Daily Bible readings

Deuteronomy 18:9–13 – Detestable practices

'Detestable practices' are condemned in Scripture. Many people today are drawn into the occult. You may find yourself helping them. Verse 13 reminds us of the need to be blameless before the Lord. Good practice in the Christian ministry of healing is very important.

Ephesians 6:10–20 – The whole armour of God

Our strength is 'in the Lord and in his mighty power'. We stand against 'the spiritual forces of evil in the heavenly realms'. We neither rush unadvisedly into action, nor flee when confronted with such powers. Continuous prayer must underpin all that we do. Pray for grace to maintain such prayer.

2 Corinthians 10:3–5 – The power of spiritual weapons

Paul defends his ministry to his readers. His own testimony reminds us that we have to wage spiritual battles, not with human effort, but with divine power that can demolish strongholds, arguments and all false ideas that set themselves up against God.

Mark 6:31 – Verse for contemplation

Jesus constantly seeks times of quiet for prayer and refreshment in the midst of his busy life. As we begin to be used by him in this ministry we will need to follow his example. 'Come with me by yourselves to a quiet place and get some rest.'

Luke 6:17–19 – The power to heal

Another of the summaries of the healing ministry of Jesus. Luke draws attention to the power which was coming from him (verse 19) which was healing them all (cf. Luke 5:17b). When Jesus sends his disciples out to 'preach the kingdom and heal the sick', he gives them power and authority. In what ways is God preparing you at this time to handle the power and authority which is part of the ministry of healing?

Chunk readings

James 1:1–3:12

James 3:13–5:20

James is not writing about how to become a Christian, but rather how to live as one. His short, practical letter contains no fewer than 54 direct commands. Praying for healing must be set in the context of an ongoing disciplined Christian life. James spells out some of the necessities of such a life. This most practical of all the epistles ends with instructions about praying for the sick (James 5:13–end).

▶ **Notes**

9 Moving on in the Christian ministry of healing

▸ Healing of the memories and emotions

The importance of forgiveness. Is God calling you to develop a particular facet of the Christian ministry of healing (eg, listening skills)?

Draft a Christian healing policy for your church, thinking about the place, frequency and type of healing services that you might hold.

▸ The church as a 'place of healing'

Who is the architect, the foundation, the power supply, the bricks? What constitutes the mortar?

The church is

- a cleansing place
- a place for living
- a place for feeding
- a place for resting
- a sending place

Daily Bible readings

 ## 1 Corinthians 13 – The primacy of love

Paul writes in Romans 5:5 that God's love is shed abroad in our hearts through the Holy Spirit he has given us. We all need to receive God's love. We must also be prepared to give his love to others.

 ## Matthew 10:1–20 – Called and equipped for his service

Jesus never promised that his disciples would have an easy time. Sometimes the disciples would not be welcomed, and sometimes persecuted. However, Christ goes with us in this work, and he will never leave us or forsake us. Let us take courage from his promises.

 ## Luke 10:1–12 – Preach the kingdom and heal the sick

There seems to be an urgency about the way Jesus says, 'Go! I am sending you out like lambs among wolves' (v3). He will always give us grace to do the tasks he appoints for us.

 ## Acts 3:6 – Verse for contemplation

'What I have I give you.' Pray that you will be able to give to others what God has given you.

 ## Revelation 22 – Ultimate healing

The river of the water of life will bring healing to the nations and abolish the curse that is on the world. Jesus is coming soon! The signs and wonders that take place as a result of our faithfulness and love for those who are suffering, are like the trumpet calls of the heralds to his coming.

 **Chunk readings**

 John chapters 1–3

 John chapters 4–5

The deceptively simple themes of light, truth, life and love are the primary colours which John uses to paint his unique picture of Christ. We must not be deceived by the gentleness of much of John's writing, with his emphasis on love, for he was also a man of great toughness. He was combating dangerous cults which were flourishing at the time. Today Christians have to be quite clear that the only true healing is a living relationship with Jesus Christ. He alone is our Lord and Saviour. He alone can bring us to the Father. He alone can fill us with the Holy Spirit of God. He alone will come again. Even so, come, Lord Jesus!

▶ Notes

A The questionnaire

1. Have you prayed with someone specifically for their healing?

   Often ❑   Occasionally ❑   Never   ❑

2. Has this course encouraged you to pray for the sick more frequently?

   Yes   ❑   Not certain   ❑   No   ❑

3. Has it helped you understand the Christian ministry of healing?

   A lot   ❑   A little   ❑   Not at all ❑

4. If it has, what insights have you found most helpful?
   1.
   2.
   3.

5. Have you ever been involved in some form of healing practice which is not Christian, but outside normal medical methods?

   Yes   ❑   No   ❑

7. If yes, what was it?

8. Are you sure that you have been filled with the power of the
   Holy Spirit?
   Yes   ❑   Unsure   ❑   No   ❑

9. Have you ever experienced gifts of the Holy Spirit?
   Never ❑   Occasionally ❑   Often   ❑
   Not certain   ❑

B The accounts of healing in the ministry of Jesus

Special events	Matthew	Mark	Luke	John
Man with unclean spirit		1:21–28	4:31–37	
Peter's mother-in-law	8:14–15	1:30–31	4:38–39	
Man with skin disease	8:2–4	1:40–42	5:12–14	
The paralysed man	9:2–8	2:3–12	5:17–26	
Man with withered hand	12:9–14	3:1–6	6:6–11	
Gadarene demoniac	8:28–34	5:1–17	8:26–39	
Woman with chronic bleeding	9:20–22	5:24–34	8:43–48	
Syro-Phoenician woman	15:21–28	7:24–30		
Deaf and dumb man		7:31–37		
Blind man		8:22–26		
Child with evil spirit	17:14–18	9:14–27	9:38–43	
Bartimaeus (sight restored)		10:46–52		
Centurion's servant	8:5–13		7:1–10	
Dumb demoniac	9:32–34			
Blind and dumb demoniac	12:22		11:14	
Woman bound by Satan			13:10–13	
Man with dropsy			14:1–4	
Ten lepers			17:11–19	
Malchus's ear			22:49–51	
Nobleman's son				4:46–53
The cripple at the pool				5:1–15
Man born blind				9:1–7 ff

Summaries of healings

After the Sabbath	8:16–17	1:32–34	4:40–41	
Many demons		1:39		

	Matthew	Mark	Luke	John
Multitudes follow Jesus	15:30	3:8–10	6:17–19	6:2
A few miracles	13:58	6:5–6		
'All who touched him'	14:36	6:56		
A summary before teaching	4:23		6:17–19	
'Go tell John' many healed	11:4–5		7:21–22	
Crowds	9:35		9:11	
	14:14		5:15	
	19:2			

Raising of the dead

	Matthew	Mark	Luke	John
Jairus's daughter	9:18 ff	5:22ff	8:40 ff	
Widow's son			7:11–17	
Lazarus				11:1–44

APPENDIX

C Prayer of commitment

Leader: Do you turn to Christ?
Response: I turn to Christ.
Leader: Do you repent of your sins?
Response: I repent of my sins.
Leader: Do you renounce evil?
Response: I renounce evil.

Heavenly Father, I want to belong to you from now on. I want to be freed from the dominion of darkness and the rule of Satan, and I want to enter into your kingdom and be part of your people. I will turn from all wrongdoing. I ask you to forgive all the sins that I have committed. I offer my life to you, and I promise to obey you as my Lord. I ask you to baptise me in the Holy Spirit and to release the gifts of the Spirit in my life. In the name of Jesus. Amen.

You may wish to discuss this prayer privately with the leader of your group. If it is the tradition of your church, you may want to make a full sacramental confession of your sins some time before making the prayer of commitment. In particular, involvement in any occult methods of healing must be renounced totally. Our healing is in the mighty name of Jesus Christ and in him alone.

D Guidelines for good practice

The following is an extract from The House of Bishop's Draft Guidelines for Good Practice in *A Time to Heal* (Church House Publishing 2000):

The healing ministry is Jesus' ministry entrusted to us, always to be exercised with reverence, love and compassion. The guiding principle is to recognize the presence of God in those receiving this ministry and honour his presence in them.

1. **Prayer and preparation.** The healing ministry is based on prayer in the name of Jesus Christ; those involved in this ministry should be prayerful, regularly practising Christians who acknowledge his healing love and are willing to pray and listen for guidance in order to minister appropriately to others.
2. **Safety.** All reasonable steps should be taken to ensure the safety of the person receiving this ministry. People have a right to know what is being provided and how they will be ministered to.
3. **Accountability and diocesan regulations.** Everyone involved in the healing ministry needs clear lines of accountability to recognize who holds relevant authority within their parish church. All reasonable steps should be taken by those involved to ensure their awareness of current law as it applies to this ministry, for example data protection; informed consent. Legal liability issues must be considered from an insurance

viewpoint. Existing diocesan regulations should also be followed.

4. **Training.** Individuals should receive appropriate training in this ministry and be kept up to date with developments and its ecumenical expression. Healing team leaders must ensure that members have opportunities for training and a common understanding of good practice.

5. **Competence and boundaries.** Persons in this ministry should be aware of their personal limitations and ensure that they are properly prepared and fit to be involved. If fitness is doubtful or compromised or there is a conflict of interests, they should withdraw from ministering to others. Professional boundaries with health care professionals and chaplaincies should be observed.

6. **Personal conduct.** The healing ministry is part of the message of the gospel; the personal conduct of everyone involved should encourage confidence in this ministry and not undermine it. Language, personal hygiene, general appearance, body language and touch used by those ministering should be appropriate, considerate and courteous towards those receiving it. No one should be ministered to against their will.

7. **Confidentiality and public statements.** People's privacy and dignity should be respected and protected. Any limitations to confidentiality should be explained in advance and any disclosure should be restricted to relevant information. It should be conveyed only to appropriate people, normally with the parishioner's consent, and not misused in any way.

8. **Counselling and psychotherapy.** These specific treatments, as distinct from pastoral care and listening, should only be provided by accredited counsellors and therapists who adhere to the codes of ethics and practice of their regulatory organizations and who have professional insurance cover.

9. **Deliverance.** The House of Bishops' guidelines (1975)

should be followed and diocesan advisors consulted when necessary.

10. **Partnership.** The healing ministry should be carried out in cooperation, where appropriate, with chaplains and representatives of our ecumenical partners, and those involved in professional and voluntary health care, whilst recognizing that they may be bound by other codes of conduct.

E Ten principles for helping people who have been involved in the occult

1. Enthrone God, not the 'principalities and powers' (Deuteronomy 20:1–4; 2 Chronicles 20:15).
2. We minister from the victory of Christ; we do not fight for a victory (Colossians 2:13–15; John 12:31).
3. Rely upon God's active help through his word (Luke 4:1–13); his authority (Luke 9:1–2); his gifts (1 Corinthians 12).
4. Do not let the devil set the agenda. The team makes the decisions about the timing and ministry style. Buy time by binding any spirits so that they can cause no harm until appropriate ministry is available. At the same time, signal to the person coming for prayer that they are being taken seriously.
5. Work in teams – this avoids spiritual pride and false accusation (Ephesians 6).
6. Do not overreact. Many people coming to faith today have been involved in the occult at some time. Not all unexplainable phenomena are of the devil. Avoid at all cost terms like 'possession' and 'exorcism'. Be aware that mental illness can produce very bizarre behaviour.
7. Deliverance is into Jesus as well as away from evil.

8. Realise that there are degrees of occult influence. Much is fairly minor, but occasionally we can encounter more serious manifestations where the victim is no longer free to be the person God wants them to be.

9. Know yourself and recognise your limitations.

10. Operate within the framework and guidelines of your church. In the Anglican church such matters must be referred to the parish priest, who will seek guidance from the bishop or his representative in this ministry.